this is the garden next to
the house

there are some fuzzbuzzes

in the garden

---

write

some fuzzbuzzes are in the garden

these are the fuzzbuzzes

the fuzzbuzzes play in
the garden next to the house

---

draw the garden

draw some fuzzbuzzes in it

write
the fuzzbuzzes play in the garden

up into the tree
goes the first fuzzbuzz

it is an apple tree

there are some red and green
apples on this tree

---

draw the apple tree

next draw some apples on it

now colour it in

write
a fuzzbuzz is up in the apple tree

the next fuzzbuzz comes to play

he is under the apple tree

he jumps onto the yellow mattress

now he jumps up and down

this is fun

it is good fun

---

write

a fuzzbuzz jumps onto the mattress

now the first fuzzbuzz
drops an apple

down comes the apple

---

draw a big apple

colour it red and green

write
the first fuzzbuzz drops an apple

down comes the apple

it drops onto the fuzzbuzz
under the tree

now he is mad

he goes up the garden
and into the house

out comes the fuzzbuzz
with a big black and red umbrella

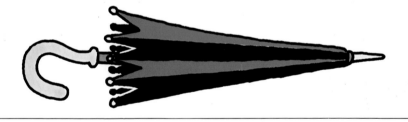

---

draw this big umbrella

colour it black and red

write
this umbrella is black and red

he jumps onto the yellow mattress

now the big umbrella goes up

up and down goes the fuzzbuzz

---

draw the fuzzbuzz jumping
up and down with the umbrella

write
up goes the big umbrella

this fuzzbuzz is mad now

he jumps up and down in the tree

---

draw this fuzzbuzz jumping
up and down in the apple tree

write

now this fuzzbuzz is mad

down come the apples

down to the big umbrella

it is good fun

---

write

the apples come down

draw and colour this

now these fuzzbuzzes come out
to play on the yellow mattress

---

draw these fuzzbuzzes

write
these fuzzbuzzes come out to play

down come the apples

up and down go the fuzzbuzzes

this is good fun

---

draw this and colour it in

write
it is good fun